The Swimmers

by Bobby Lynn Maslen
pictures by John R. Maslen

Scholastic Inc.

New York • Toronto • London • Auckland • Sydney • Mexico City • New Delhi • Hong Kong • Buenos Aires

Available Bob Books®:

Set 1: Beginning Readers — With consistent new sounds added gradually, your new reader is gently introduced to all the letters of the alphabet. They can soon say, "I read the whole book!®"

Set 2: Advancing Beginners — The use of three-letter words and consistent vowel sounds in slightly longer stories build skill and confidence.

Set 3: Word Families — Consonant blends, endings and a few sight words advance reading skills while the use of word families keep reading manageable.

Set 4: Complex Words — Longer books and complex words engage young readers as proficiency advances.

Set 5: Long Vowels — Silent e and other vowel blends build young readers' vocabulary and aptitude.

Bob Books® Collections:

Collection 1 — Includes Set 1: Beginning Readers and part of Set 2: Advancing Beginners

Collection 2 — Includes part of Set 2: Advancing Beginners and Set 3: Word Families

Collection 3 — Includes Set 4: Complex Words and Set 5: Long Vowels

Ask for Bob Books at your local bookstore, or visit www.bobbooks.com.

ISBN 0-545-02701-2

6 5 4 3 2   10 11/0

Printed in China   68
This edition first printing, September 2007

It was summer. Pop, Stan, and Jim went to the pond.

Jim wanted to swim.
Stan wanted to swim.

Jim slipped into the pond.
Stan jumped into the pond.

Jim and Stan swam to a log.

"Step on the log, Jim," called Stan.
Jim slipped. "Jump on the log, Stan,"
called Jim. Stan slid.

"Stop! Stop!" called Pop.
The log spun.

"Help, Pop," called Jim.
"Help us stop, Pop," called Stan.

Pop wanted to help Jim and Stan.
Pop jumped onto the log, but
the log was a trap.

Into the pond went Pop.
Pop got wet.

Pop, Stan, and Jim got out of the pond.

"Sit in the sun, Jim. Sit in a warm spot, Stan," said Pop. "Sit in the warm sun, Pop," called Stan and Jim.

The three swimmers went to
a sunny spot. The wet swimmers
sat happily on a warm spot
in the sun.

The End

Book 4 adds:

Blends:
sw	–	swim
sp	–	spun
tr	–	trap
rm	–	warm

Long Vowel:
ee	–	three